My Dad Says ™

A "drive safe" book for adults ... and their kids!

By Debbie Middleton-Hope   Illustrated by Lisa Dawood

In co-operation with

THE CITY OF CALGARY, ROADS

and

THE CALGARY POLICE SERVICE

Written by Debbie Middleton-Hope
Illustrated by Lisa Dawood
© Copyright 2002 by Everytown Inc.
All rights reserved.

Printed in Canada by Friesens Printers, Altona, MB
Layout and design by SunRidge Designs, Armstrong, BC 1 800 230-1623

National Library of Canada Cataloguing in Publication Data

Middleton-Hope, Debbie, 1953-
My dad says

"In co-operation with Calgary Roads and the
Calgary Police Service" – t.p.
ISBN 0-9687565-1-4

1. Traffic safety–Juvenile literature.
I. Dawood, Lisa, 1970-
II. Calgary (Alta.). Calgary Roads.
III. Calgary (Alta.). Police Service. IV. Title.

PS8576.I283M88 2002   j363.1'25   C2002-910175-1
PR9199.4.M52M88 2002

Acknowledgements

Roxanne Beaubien

Detective Susan Brown

Dan Dorsey, Retired

Staff Sergeant Gary Loughery

Inspector Joan McCallum

Cam Nelson, Traffic Safety Coordinator

Sergeant Steve Patterson

Cara-Lynn Stelmack

A Message From General Manager
A.R. Andreasen, P. Eng.
The City of Calgary, Roads

As the General Manager of the City of Calgary, Roads, I am pleased to be associated with a project that focuses on the safe and responsible use of the transportation system. The City of Calgary, Roads' main objective is to provide a safe and efficient transportation network, but we cannot do it alone.

Traffic safety is the responsibility of everyone. From the five-year-old children, riding their bicycles on the sidewalk in front of their homes, to their parents and grandparents, to their brothers and sisters, to their aunts and uncles and to everyone who drives on the roadways. Each of us has a role to play in making the roads safe.

The City of Calgary, Roads has formed partnerships with many different agencies. We work closely with the Calgary Health Region, the Calgary Police Service, the Alberta Insurance Industry, the Alberta Motor Association (AMA) and the local school boards to develop safety programs to keep our roads safe.

In spite of all these agencies and all of the people involved in traffic safety, we still have thousands of collisions occurring on our roadways in which hundreds of people are injured and dozens of people are killed each year.

This project is new for us. We can try to build better and safer roadways. We can work with our partners to make the roadway environment safer for everyone. However, with this book, we are trying to help the people using the roadways learn to use them a little better. If both parents and children learn to use the roads the way the roads were supposed to be used, the transportation world would be a safer place.

It is for these reasons we are extremely pleased to support this educational program, and look forward to safer streets thanks to the drivers of tomorrow.

A Message From
Chief Jack Beaton
Calgary Police Service

Speeding and other traffic issues are among the top policing concerns of Calgarians. So it is with great pride that I introduce you to this innovative, interactive and educational book for parents and their young children.

It is never too early to teach our children road safety lessons, lessons they need to know as pedestrians or cyclists, and ones that will serve them well as future drivers. This book is also a good refresher for parents. Our children often learn from watching us. If we demonstrate bad driving habits, that is the lesson we will pass on to our children.

The Calgary Police Service is involved in many traffic safety strategies and we are pleased to support this project. This is just one example of the many partnerships the Service is involved in, which encourage community and traffic safety.

Inspector Debbie Middleton-Hope has once again done a wonderful job in taking her 22-plus years of policing experience and channelling it into a book that is not only entertaining for children, but also important in helping parents teach their children street safety. Debbie's first book, "My Mom Says: a safety book for kids", proved to be an effective tool for many parents. I am confident "My Dad Says: A "drive safe" book for adults... and their kids", will be just as effective and successful.

Congratulations to Debbie and also to you, you've taken an important step in continuing to teach your children well!

How to Use This Book

1. Congratulate yourself for taking the steps to teach your child personal safety. This book is a tool for both you and your child.

2. Read the book in its entirety before sharing it with your child. Be comfortable with the contents of the book.

3. Sit down and read the book out loud to your child. Take the time to look at all that is happening in the illustrations on each page. Talk about each picture and emphasize how Buddy is learning about safety.

4. As you read the book to your child, think about your own driving habits. What are you teaching your child about safety as he/she watches you drive your vehicle? Are you demonstrating respect for others?

5. Talk about the importance of staying safe and driving safely with your family.

6. Sing the safety song with your child as you are travelling in your vehicle.

7. Play is a wonderful tool to teach a child. Play the driving game at the back of the book to reinforce the safe driving rules.

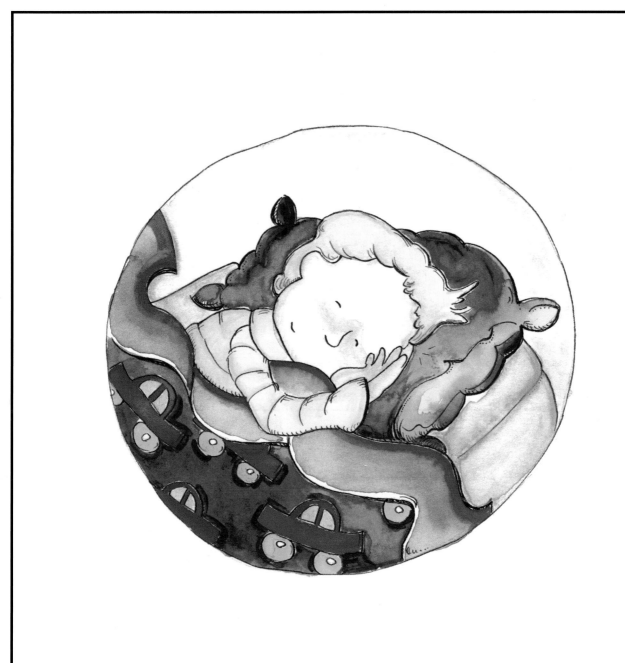

Buddy awoke with a stretch
and a yawn as the sun shone
brightly over Everytown.
Today was Safety Day at school
and Buddy's dad was going to
show Buddy all about being safe.
It was going to be a great day!

Buddy was excited. He could hardly wait to see what his dad had planned.
He found his dad waiting for him downstairs. It was time to learn about safety.

"Get ready my son,
to learn and have fun.
With me as your guide,
let's go for a ride."

"The best advice I can give,
is you learn what you live.
I want you to see,
safety is important to me."

11

"I like to start slow,
so I know where to go.
If you know the directions,
you won't have to ask questions."

Buddy was surprised at all the things his dad knew about being safe. They talked about the importance of following all the traffic signals, stopping at stop signs, how to be careful when making a left turn and not to follow other cars too closely.

Buddy watched out of his window of the car
and saw many people who were not driving safely.
He was glad his dad followed all the rules.
It made him feel safe. Buddy was proud of his dad.

"If you want to be cool,
just follow the rules.
It's important to mention,
you must pay attention."

"There's no real need,
to go over the speed.
Keep safety in mind,
and please take your time."

Buddy learned a lot about being safe
from watching his dad drive his car.
Buddy knew his dad followed
the safety rules because
he loved Buddy very much.
Driving safely keeps children
from getting hurt.
Learning about safety
makes Buddy feel more important.

19

The lights serve a purpose,
go by the colours.
Obey all the traffic signs,
be respectful of others.

Safe driving is important,
pay close attention.
The key to safe driving,
is practise prevention.

Collisions can happen,
and sometimes they're bad.
So when I get a car,
I'll drive safe like my dad!

Buddy

21

DAD'S SAFETY PLAN

1. Always wear a seatbelt.
2. Follow the rules of the road.
3. Obey the traffic lights.
4. Be respectful to others.

Everytown Safety Song

Music by Kathleen Woods 2001

Follow the rules, drive safe! Follow the rules, drive safe!

If you want to be cool, Just follow the rules.

Follow the rules, drive safe!

STATISTICS

Motor vehicle collisions affect people of all ages and are the leading cause of injury and death in children.

89% of traffic collisions are caused by driver error.

Occupants who were using seatbelts at the time of collision were injured less often (14%) than occupants who were not using restraints (37%).

The top major causes of vehicle collisions in Alberta are following too closely (26.7%), running off the road (14.2%) and turning left across the path of an oncoming vehicle (12.4%).

The afternoon rush hour period accounts for the highest number of crashes.

(Alberta Traffic Collision Statistics 2000)

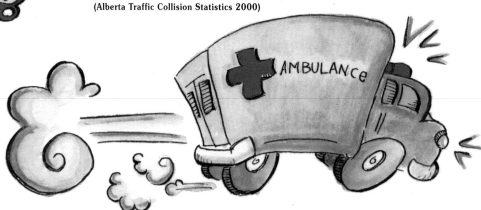

About the Author...

A mother of four and proud grandmother of one, Debbie Middleton-Hope has been an officer with the Calgary Police Service for more than two decades. She walked the beat as a constable, investigated crimes such as child abuse, robbery and prostitution as a Detective and Staff Sergeant, and now runs the Administration Section as an Inspector. Raised in southern Alberta, her first children's book was published in 2000. "My Mom Says: A safety book for kids", has since been developed into a personal safety program for young children by Safe & Sound Calgary.

Debbie has won several awards for her crime prevention work directed at protecting children and vulnerable people. These honours include a 2001 Alberta Crime Prevention Award, 2001 YWCA Woman of Distinction Award and being named a Woman of Vision by Global Television. "My Dad Says: A "drive safe" book for adults and their kids", was inspired by the birth of Debbie's grandson.

About the Illustrator...

Lisa remembers as a child the many trips her family would take in their big brown Oldsmobile! Three sisters in the back of the car fighting for their own space, her mom making funny faces to pass the time and her dad an example of true patience in the midst of it all. Even today, her dad's respectful and positive actions speak much louder than words. Now all grown up, with her own girls as "precious cargo", Lisa understands how important it is to follow her dad's example on, and off the road.

When not drawing pictures, Lisa enjoys time with her husband Mike and their girls Sharayah and Lauryn in their home of Edmonton, Alberta.

Precious Cargo

Drive Safe

 # Dear Parent

The most precious gift of all is the gift of a child. Yet we think nothing about putting that child into our vehicle and breaking all the rules of the road. The precious cargo we are transporting is seldom considered as we drink our coffee, talk on the cell phone or search for the favourite CD. Our inattention could easily be putting our children's life in jeopardy. Funny how we never think of children needing protection from their parents' unsafe driving habits.

I'll never forget the first traffic collision I attended as a police officer in which a child was hurt. Her father had failed to stop at a stop sign and was broadsided by another vehicle. As she lay on the ground bleeding, crying and shaking with fear, I thought the ambulance was never going to get there. It was a very helpless feeling.

With the birth of my grandson in the spring of 2001, I was once again reminded just how precious and innocent little people are. With his birth came the birth of "My Dad Says: A "drive safe" book for adults and their kids". I want him to be safe from all the bad drivers on the road.

An average of 400 people are killed and 23,000 persons injured in collisions each year in Alberta. Motor vehicle collisions are the leading cause of death for Albertans under the age of 30. So not only are children being physically hurt by traffic collisions, in some cases they are also left parentless.

Although "My Dad Says" is a children's book, my audience is really you, the parent. I want to remind you to focus on your driving habits and drive safe. In analysing traffic collisions, the human error factors have been estimated as high as 89%. When you are behind the wheel of a vehicle, don't let the distractions of everyday living result in a lifetime of pain and regret.

So what can you as a parent do to cut your risk of being in a collision? If you always wear your seatbelt, follow the rules of the road, obey the traffic lights and are respectful to others just as it states in "My Dad Says," you'll definitely increase your chances of keeping you and your children safe.

Before the flight, buckle up tight. Seatbelts save lives. As the driver it is your responsibility to ensure every passenger under the age of 16 is wearing a seatbelt or is harnessed in a child safety seat. It is the law. A seatbelt will keep you and your children from being thrown around like a rag doll in the event of a collision. No matter how short the distance, always wear your seatbelt. Another important fact for you as a parent to know is the back seat is the safest place for your child. Children 12 and under should sit in the back seat away from the air bag. Only children over 60 pounds are grown enough to use a seatbelt. Until that time, children should be seated in a car seat that is appropriate for their body weight.

Retired Staff Sergeant Dan Dorsey recalls a time when he didn't wear a seatbelt. He had been a cop for many years and had gotten into the habit of leaving it off in case he had to exit the police vehicle in a hurry. One day he had to make a short trip into town and asked his two boys if they would like to go with him. They refused. When he questioned why, they told him flat out it was because he didn't wear his seatbelt. Both boys started to cry and expressed their concern for his safety. Dan realized the impact his habit was having on his two young sons and what a lesson he had learned from them that day. From that day forward, he reassured his boys he would never go without his seatbelt again.

If you want to be cool, just follow the rules. Drivers are required to pass a written exam on the rules of the road before a licence is issued, so ignorance of the law is not an excuse. If drivers followed the rules, collisions would be reduced. The laws are there for everyone's safety. Following too closely (26.7%) is the top driver error contributing to injury collisions. Are you leaving a safe distance between your vehicle and the vehicle in front of you? Driving off the road (14.2%), turning left across the path of oncoming traffic (12.4%), stop sign violations (9.2%) and disobeying traffic signals (8.2%) are the major driver errors in injury collisions. The majority of collisions are preventable.

It's important to mention, you must pay attention. It is easy to get distracted, but it only takes a moment of inattention for a car to become a deadly machine. Keep your hands on the wheel and your mind on the task at hand. Pull over to use the cellular phone or to settle a disagreement between siblings. Driving is not the time to be putting on your make-up, reading a book, looking in the back seat or shaving.

Sergeant Steve Patterson had just exited his police car and was about to enter the day care to do a safety presentation to a group of young children. A young boy waved at him and presented him with a big smile. A few seconds later, Sergeant Patterson heard the sickening sound of squealing tires and a loud thud. His heart raced as he ran to the broken child lying on the roadway. The driver had failed to see the little boy with the big smile in the crosswalk.

There's really no need to go over the speed. Travel at the posted speed limit. It is better to get to your destination a few minutes late than not to get there at all. Speed limits are not set randomly but are a calculation of the highest possible speed a car can travel safely given ideal road conditions. A driver's ability to steer the vehicle and to stop safely in an emergency are affected by speed. Drivers who travel above the posted speed limits are putting lives at risk. Speeding is one of the leading contributors in collisions. Remember to slow down.

Inspector Joan McCallum watched the approaching BMW in her rearview mirror as it was speeding and cutting in and out of traffic on the roadway. She couldn't believe it when the driver sped past her. She initiated the emergency lights and siren, and was eventually able to get the attention of the driver who pulled over to the side of the road. She approached the driver who immediately blurted out that his son was late for his eye doctor's appointment. Inspector McCallum looked in the back seat and saw a young child who was watching her with interest. "So are you saying it is your son's fault you're speeding?" asked the Inspector. The driver quickly realized the lameness of his excuse. After the proper documentation was exchanged, the Inspector leaned down to speak to the child, explaining that his dad needed help with his driving and could he please remind him to slow down. The child smiled at her and agreed.

Always use your head. Stop at the red. Red means stop, green means go and yellow means slow down to clear the intersection, not speed up to get through the intersection before the light turns red. How often have you observed a vehicle accelerate at a yellow light only to see the driver again at the next red light? Obey the traffic lights!

Don't forget, show others respect. The driver who continuously cuts other drivers off, makes unsafe lane changes, speeds, follows too closely and disobeys traffic signs and signals is demonstrating aggressive driving behaviour. Aggressive driving is often the result of individuals who take their anger, resentment and frustration behind the wheel. An aggressive state of mind affects everyone's safety. Share the road and be courteous to the other drivers around you. Practice being courteous, cautious and use common sense.

Detective Susan Brown couldn't believe her eyes when she observed the behaviour of the woman driving next to her. The woman was clearly upset at the adjacent driver for she was yelling and swearing at him through the open window. The woman was visibly out of control as her profanity intensified. Susan happened to look in the back seat of the woman's vehicle and to her dismay, she saw two tiny pairs of eyes watching their mother.

Imagine how frightening it is for a child to be with a parent and be exposed to yelling, screaming, foul language and a barrage of obscene gestures. Imagine how much more frightening it must be when it is the child's parent demonstrating the aggressive behaviour. Imagine what the child is learning about safe driving and respect for others.

Our children are the drivers of the future. As parents, you are their teachers. Be sure to teach them well. Collisions are preventable. Prevention is the key. Drive defensively and help reduce the number of collisions that occur on our roads.

Remember the **Precious Cargo** you are transporting and **Drive Safe!**

References:
www.saferoads.com
www.ama.ab.ca

Travel Tips for Parents

It is not easy to sit still for longer than ten minutes when you are a child, especially if you are buckled in and there is nothing to do. Keeping your children entertained while travelling in the car will help reduce the stress for everyone. Here are some tips to make your travel time more pleasant, so you as the driver, can pay attention to the road.

- Have plenty of healthy snacks on hand, especially after school or an activity. The snack will help take the edge off until you get home.

- Bring plenty of children's music to listen to and don't be afraid to sing along with the favourites. The "Everytown Safety Song" is a memorable little tune and should be on the Top 10 list.

- Play car games such as "I Spy", "Twenty-one Questions" or a counting game. See who can tell the funniest riddle. Get more car game ideas off of the website.

- Bring along your child's favourite small toy, book, crayons and paper. Bring things to keep them amused for travelling in a car can be boring.

- Engage your children in conversation. Find out about their day, their friends, their favourite things, etc. Use this time to form a bond with your child.

- Talk to them about safety. Red means stop, green means go and yellow means slow. Note how many different traffic signs are on the route. Take advantage of this time to develop a parent/child bond.

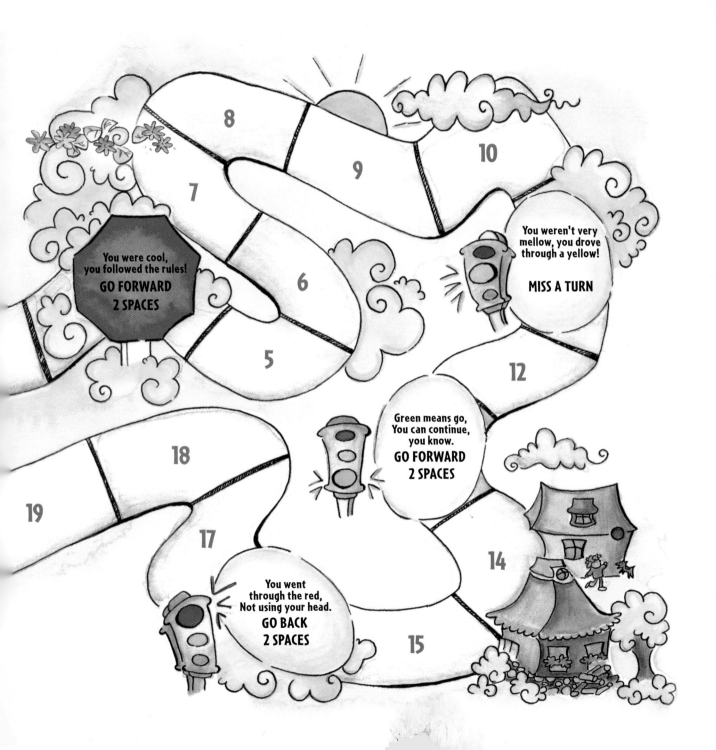

SAFETY GAME INSTRUCTIONS

1. Cut out all the game pieces on the darkened lines and fold cars on dotted lines.

2. You will need a paper clip and a paper fastener.

3. Slide the paper clip onto the fastener and push the fastener through the center of the number wheel.

4. Give the paper clip a spin and move your car forward on the board, following the stops along the way.

5. Alternative to cars and spinner:
   Make your own game pieces with buttons or coins. To move around the board use a die or flip a coin. Heads move one space, tails move two spaces.

6. Take turns, discuss the safety stops on the board, and...

   HAVE FUN!!

SAFETY GAME CUT-OUTS